Table of Contents

© 2004 ETR Associates. Revised 2013. All rights reserved. Published by ETR, 100 Enterprise Way, Suite G300, Scotts Valley, CA 95066. www.etr.org. This *Student Workbook* is a part of ETR's *HealthSmart* K–12 program. ISBN 978-1-56071-868-0.

All About A.J.

Directions: Define the terms in Part 1. Then, in Part 2, use what you've learned about aspects of sexuality to create a healthy sexuality profile for a fictional high school student.

▶ Part 1

Define these terms.

What's the definition of *sexuality?*

_____

What's sexual *abstinence?*

_____

What does it mean to be *sexually active?*

_____

What's *sexual orientation?*

_____

What's *gender identity?*

_____

What does it mean to be *transgender?*

_____

What are *gender roles?*

_____

_____

▶ Part 2

Create a profile for A.J. that demonstrates healthy sexuality.

A.J. is a junior at your high school. A.J. is a pretty good student who enjoys playing music and spending time with friends. A.J. is also a teen who has a healthy sense of sexuality.

A.J.'s gender is

☐ female   ☐ male   ☐ transgender female   ☐ transgender male

A.J. is sexually attracted to

☐ males   ☐ females   ☐ both   ☐ neither

Is A.J. currently in a relationship with anyone? _____

All About A.J.

(continued)

What's one of A.J.'s values around sexuality? _____

_____

_____

_____

Is A.J. abstinent or sexually active? _____

Why did A.J. make this choice? _____

_____

_____

_____

What kinds of things does A.J. do to take care of his/her body and sexual health? _____

_____

_____

_____

What's an example of a healthy way A.J. listens or communicates about sex? _____

_____

_____

_____

Based on the profile you created, describe at least 3 positive effects a healthy sense of sexuality will have on A.J.'s current and/or future relationships.

1. _____

_____

2. _____

_____

3. _____

_____

Self-Check

☐ I wrote clear definitions of all the terms.

☐ I created a profile that shows a healthy sense of sexuality.

☐ I described at least 3 positive effects a healthy sense of sexuality will have on A.J.'s relationships.

Respect for Sexual Differences
Campaign Plan—Part 1

> **Directions:** Work on your own to answer these questions.

1 **Is a lack of respect for different aspects of sexuality a problem at our school?**

☐ Yes   ☐ No

2 **What's the evidence behind your yes or no answer?**

_____

_____

3 **If your response was yes:**

■ What are at least 2 negative consequences this problem is causing?

_____

_____

■ What would be at least 3 benefits of changing the school environment to one of respect?

_____

_____

_____

4 **If your response was no:**

■ What are at least 2 negative consequences or problems that are prevented because of an environment of respect?

_____

_____

■ What are at least 3 benefits students at your school enjoy because this isn't a problem?

_____

_____

_____

5 **Describe at least 2 ways people at your school already show or could show respect for different aspects of sexuality.**

_____

_____

_____

_____

Self-Check

☐ I listed at least 3 benefits of respecting differences in aspects of sexuality.

☐ I listed at least 2 negative consequences caused by lack of respect for differences.

☐ I described at least 2 ways people could show respect for differences.

Respect for Sexual Differences
Campaign Plan—Part 2

> **Directions:** Work with your group to design a communication strategy or tool that can be used to encourage incoming freshmen and new students to show respect for the different aspects of sexuality expressed by their fellow students. Fill out the points below to help you plan your campaign. Be sure to take a clear stand and design a strategy or tool that will appeal and make sense to your audience.

1 **The goal of our Respect for Sexual Differences campaign is to: (check one)**

☐ Encourage students to continue to do things that show a respect for different aspects of sexuality.

☐ Help correct a problem by persuading students of the importance of acting in ways that show respect for different aspects of sexuality.

2 **The communication strategy we have chosen is a: (check one)**

☐ Bookmark or button campaign   ☐ Page on the school's website

☐ Information leaflet or brochure   ☐ Banner

☐ Series of daily announcements   ☐ Other: _____.

☐ Article in the school newspaper

Here's how it will work (describe how you will implement your strategy):

_____

_____

_____

_____

_____

_____

_____

_____

_____

_____

_____

_____

_____

_____

(continued)

Respect for Sexual Differences
Campaign Plan—Part 2

(continued)

3 This is the message or combination of messages we'll communicate to others to encourage respect for sexual differences:

_____

_____

_____

_____

_____

_____

4 Here's why this message will appeal to or convince our audience:

_____

_____

_____

_____

_____

5 These are the 3 talking points we could use to convince the school administration to support our campaign. (*Note*: Be sure to include benefits of respecting different aspects of sexuality and negative consequences of not doing so.)

1. _____

_____

_____

2. _____

_____

_____

3. _____

_____

_____

_____

Self-Check
- ☐ We created a persuasive campaign that has a clear goal.
- ☐ We designed a communication strategy and a plan for how it will work.
- ☐ We created a persuasive message that will appeal to our audience.
- ☐ We included 3 talking points to convince the administration to support our campaign.

HEALTHSmart. High School

My Advice About Sexual Responsibility

> **Directions:** Read the situation. Then choose the friend to whom you'd like to give advice, and answer the questions.

▶ Situation

You have 2 friends who want to talk about their sexual choices with you. They trust and respect you and are interested in hearing any advice or insights you might be able to share.

- **Friend A** is choosing to be sexually abstinent.
- **Friend B** is choosing to become sexually active. For friend B this means choosing to have sexual intercourse with his or her current boyfriend or girlfriend.

Write what you would say to your friend around each of these questions to help him/her understand the sexual risks and responsibilities that lie ahead.

▶ Your Advice

My advice is for: ☐ Friend A ☐ Friend B

1 Why does a person need to be responsible for his or her own sexual choices?

_____

_____

_____

_____

_____

2 What are at least 3 negative consequences of sexual activity that Friend A will avoid by being sexually abstinent?

OR

What are at least 3 negative consequences Friend B could have to deal with as a result of becoming sexually active?

_____

_____

_____

_____

_____

(continued)

My Advice About Sexual Responsibility

(continued)

3 Based on the choice your friend has made, what are at least 2 sexual limits he or she might have to set to be sexually responsible, and why is it important for your friend to set these limits?

_____

_____

_____

_____

4 What are at least 2 benefits your friend will get from being sexually responsible around his/her choice?

_____

_____

_____

5 What are at least 2 barriers that might get in the way or make it difficult for your friend to be sexually responsible after making this choice?

_____

_____

_____

6 Describe at least 3 actions your friend can take to demonstrate sexual responsibility for his/her choice.

_____

_____

_____

_____

_____

_____

_____

Self-Check

☐ I clearly explained why a person needs to be responsible for sexual choices.

☐ I described at least 3 negative consequences of sexual activity.

☐ I described at least 2 sexual limits my friend might have to set, and explained why this is important.

☐ I described at least 2 benefits of being sexually responsible.

☐ I described at least 2 things that might make sexual responsibility difficult.

☐ I described at least 3 actions that demonstrate sexual responsibility.

HEALTH *Smart* High School

Birth Control Guided Notes

> **Directions:** Fill out the first section for the birth control method your small group is learning about. Then, use the remaining sections to record the key information about each of the other methods as they are presented.

▶ **Method my group learned about:** _____

How this method works: _____

_____

Effectiveness rate: _____ if used correctly every time (perfect use)

_____ if sometimes forgotten or not used correctly

Where you get it: _____ ☐ prescription ☐ over the counter

Advantages: _____

Disadvantages: _____

Protects from: ☐ pregnancy ☐ STD/HIV   **Who uses it:** ☐ partners together ☐ person alone

▶ **Method:** _____

How this method works: _____

_____

Effectiveness rate: _____ if used correctly every time (perfect use)

_____ if sometimes forgotten or not used correctly

Where you get it: _____ ☐ prescription ☐ over the counter

Advantages: _____

Disadvantages: _____

Protects from: ☐ pregnancy ☐ STD/HIV   **Who uses it:** ☐ partners together ☐ person alone

(continued)

Birth Control Guided Notes

(continued)

▶ **Method:** _____

How this method works: _____
_____

Effectiveness rate: _____ if used correctly every time (perfect use)

_____ if sometimes forgotten or not used correctly

Where you get it: _____ ☐ prescription ☐ over the counter

Advantages: _____

Disadvantages: _____

Protects from: ☐ pregnancy ☐ STD/HIV   **Who uses it:** ☐ partners together ☐ person alone

▶ **Method:** _____

How this method works: _____
_____

Effectiveness rate: _____ if used correctly every time (perfect use)

_____ if sometimes forgotten or not used correctly

Where you get it: _____ ☐ prescription ☐ over the counter

Advantages: _____

Disadvantages: _____

Protects from: ☐ pregnancy ☐ STD/HIV   **Who uses it:** ☐ partners together ☐ person alone

▶ **Method:** _____

How this method works: _____
_____

Effectiveness rate: _____ if used correctly every time (perfect use)

_____ if sometimes forgotten or not used correctly

Where you get it: _____ ☐ prescription ☐ over the counter

Advantages: _____

Disadvantages: _____

Protects from: ☐ pregnancy ☐ STD/HIV   **Who uses it:** ☐ partners together ☐ person alone

Birth Control Guided Notes

(continued)

▶ **Method:** _____

How this method works: _____

_____

Effectiveness rate: _____ if used correctly every time (perfect use)

_____ if sometimes forgotten or not used correctly

Where you get it: _____ ☐ prescription ☐ over the counter

Advantages: _____

Disadvantages: _____

Protects from: ☐ pregnancy ☐ STD/HIV   **Who uses it:** ☐ partners together ☐ person alone

▶ **Method:** _____

How this method works: _____

_____

Effectiveness rate: _____ if used correctly every time (perfect use)

_____ if sometimes forgotten or not used correctly

Where you get it: _____ ☐ prescription ☐ over the counter

Advantages: _____

Disadvantages: _____

Protects from: ☐ pregnancy ☐ STD/HIV   **Who uses it:** ☐ partners together ☐ person alone

▶ **Method:** _____

How this method works: _____

_____

Effectiveness rate: _____ if used correctly every time (perfect use)

_____ if sometimes forgotten or not used correctly

Where you get it: _____ ☐ prescription ☐ over the counter

Advantages: _____

Disadvantages: _____

Protects from: ☐ pregnancy ☐ STD/HIV   **Who uses it:** ☐ partners together ☐ person alone

(continued)

Birth Control Guided Notes

(continued)

▶ **Method:** _____

How this method works: _____

_____

Effectiveness rate: _____ if used correctly every time (perfect use)

_____ if sometimes forgotten or not used correctly

Where you get it: _____ ☐ prescription ☐ over the counter

Advantages: _____

Disadvantages: _____

Protects from: ☐ pregnancy ☐ STD/HIV   **Who uses it:** ☐ partners together ☐ person alone

▶ **Method:** _____

How this method works: _____

_____

Effectiveness rate: _____ if used correctly every time (perfect use)

_____ if sometimes forgotten or not used correctly

Where you get it: _____ ☐ prescription ☐ over the counter

Advantages: _____

Disadvantages: _____

Protects from: ☐ pregnancy ☐ STD/HIV   **Who uses it:** ☐ partners together ☐ person alone

Birth Control Choices

Directions: Read the stories about these different young adult couples. Based on what you've learned, suggest which method would be best for each couple and explain why. Then answer the questions.

▶ Roland & Keisha

Roland and Keisha are each other's "first love." They've been together since high school, and have recently decided they're ready to start having sexual intercourse. They both want their first time to be special, but they also know they have to use birth control because they're not ready to be parents yet. Keisha feels uncomfortable about inserting something into her body, but she also thinks she should be the one in charge of the birth control because she's always been very organized and good at remembering things.

What birth control method would you recommend for this couple?

_____

Why would this method be a good choice for them?

_____

_____

_____

Where can they get this method?

_____

▶ Sarah & Jeff

Sarah and Jeff met at work and have been dating for a few months. They both had other partners in college. They like each other and enjoy spending time and having sex together, but neither one of them feels ready to make a commitment right now.

What birth control method would you recommend for this couple?

_____

Why would this method be a good choice for them?

_____

_____

Where can they get this method?

_____

(continued)

Birth Control Choices *(continued)*

▶ Mei & Jason

Mei and Jason are in their early 20s. They've both been in other relationships before, so they got tested for HIV and other STD when they started dating. Once they knew that neither of them had HIV or another STD, they felt ready to start a sexual relationship with each other. They both like being able to be spontaneous. Mei doesn't want to have to worry about taking a pill every day, and Jason told Mei he doesn't really like using a condom.

What birth control method would you recommend for this couple?

_____

Why would this method be a good choice for them?

_____

_____

_____

Where can they get this method?

_____

▶ Questions

1 **What would you say to convince all these couples of the importance of using birth control correctly and consistently (every time)?**

_____

_____

_____

_____

_____

2 **Why is it important for people who are thinking of becoming sexually active to get counseling and services around birth control?**

_____

_____

_____

_____

_____

> ### Self-Check
> ☐ I recommended the best birth control method for all 3 couples and explained why it's a good choice.
> ☐ I explained the importance of using birth control correctly and consistently.
> ☐ I explained the importance of getting counseling and services around birth control.

HEALTH *Smart.* High School

STD Checklist

How do you get it?	Chlamydia	Gonorrhea	Hepatitis B	Herpes	HPV	Syphilis	Trich
▨ unprotected sex	☐	☐	☐	☐	☐	☐	☐
▨ sharing needles	☐	☐	☐	☐	☐	☐	☐
▨ contact with sores or broken skin	☐	☐	☐	☐	☐	☐	☐
▨ genital touching	☐	☐	☐	☐	☐	☐	☐
Symptoms							
▨ pain when urinating	☐	☐	☐	☐	☐	☐	☐
▨ discharge	☐	☐	☐	☐	☐	☐	☐
▨ sores/bumps	☐	☐	☐	☐	☐	☐	☐
▨ fever, flu-like symptoms	☐	☐	☐	☐	☐	☐	☐
▨ may have no symptoms	☐	☐	☐	☐	☐	☐	☐
Can it be cured?							
▨ yes	☐	☐	☐	☐	☐	☐	☐
▨ no	☐	☐	☐	☐	☐	☐	☐
What can happen if you don't get treated?							
▨ can pass to a partner	☐	☐	☐	☐	☐	☐	☐
▨ sterility	☐	☐	☐	☐	☐	☐	☐
▨ other diseases	☐	☐	☐	☐	☐	☐	☐
▨ death	☐	☐	☐	☐	☐	☐	☐
▨ can be passed to baby in childbirth	☐	☐	☐	☐	☐	☐	☐
How can you prevent it?							
▨ not having sex	☐	☐	☐	☐	☐	☐	☐
▨ never share needles	☐	☐	☐	☐	☐	☐	☐
▨ never share razors, toothbrushes, etc.	☐	☐	☐	☐	☐	☐	☐
▨ vaccine	☐	☐	☐	☐	☐	☐	☐
How can you reduce your risk?							
▨ latex condoms	☐	☐	☐	☐	☐	☐	☐
▨ vaccine	☐	☐	☐	☐	☐	☐	☐

Understanding STDs

Directions: Use the information you learned today to answer the questions.

1 What are 3 ways STDs can be transmitted?

_____

_____

_____

2 Explain how people can reduce their risk of getting STD, including the best ways to prevent it.

_____

_____

_____

_____

3 What are at least 3 symptoms of common STDs?

_____

_____

_____

4 Why is it a problem when an STD doesn't cause symptoms?

_____

_____

_____

5 What are at least 3 short-term consequences of untreated STDs?

_____

_____

_____

6 What are at least 3 possible long-term consequences of untreated STDs?

_____

_____

_____

_____

HEALTH *Smart* High School

Understanding STDs (continued)

(7) **Match the STD to the symptoms.**

Chlamydia

Gonorrhea

Hepatitis B

Herpes

HPV

Syphilis

Trich

About a week after having sex with a new partner, Tina's genital area began to itch, and she noticed a smelly yellow-green discharge coming from her vagina.

Jonah hasn't had sex with anyone for several months, but he recently noticed some small, flat bumps on his penis.

Kyle's genital area started tingling and itching a few days ago, and now there are small blisters there.

About 3 weeks after hooking up with this guy at a party, Ana noticed she was bleeding when it wasn't time for her period, and she started to have a burning feeling when she urinated.

Alex started feeling very tired and her knees and elbows felt sore and swollen. She knew she needed to see a doctor when she noticed that her skin and the whites of her eyes were looking yellow.

Just a few days after having sex with his new girlfriend, Ty started having pain when he urinated and noticed a thick yellow discharge in his underwear.

About a month ago, Raymond noticed a sore on his penis. It didn't hurt and went away, so he decided not to worry about it. But now he's got a rash on his palms and the bottoms of his feet and feels like he might be getting the flu.

(8) **What should a person who's having symptoms or who may have been exposed to an STD do and why?**

_____

_____

_____

_____

_____

_____

_____

_____

Self-Check
- ☐ I described 3 ways STDs can be transmitted.
- ☐ I explained how to reduce the risk of STD, including the best way to prevent it.
- ☐ I listed 3 STD symptoms.
- ☐ I oxplained why it's a problem when an STD doesn't cause symptoms.
- ☐ I described 3 short-term and 3 long-term consequences of untreated STD.
- ☐ I matched the STDs to the symptoms.
- ☐ I explained what a person who has symptoms or who may have been exposed to an STD should do and why.

HIV Quiz
Fact or Myth?

> **Directions:** Read the statements about HIV. Decide whether each statement is a fact or a myth. Write **fact** or **myth** on the line in front of each statement.

_____ 1. You can get HIV by drinking from someone's glass.

_____ 2. You can get HIV from going to school with someone who has HIV.

_____ 3. A mother with HIV can pass the virus to her baby.

_____ 4. You can get HIV from toilet seats.

_____ 5. No known cases of HIV have been passed through tears or saliva.

_____ 6. HIV can be prevented.

_____ 7. HIV can be passed in blood, semen and vaginal fluids.

_____ 8. It's safe to be friends with someone who has HIV.

_____ 9. There are ways to have safer sex and reduce the risk of HIV.

_____ 10. You can get HIV from kissing someone on the lips.

_____ 11. You can get HIV from sharing needles to inject drugs or for any other reason.

_____ 12. You can get HIV from an infected person's sneeze.

_____ 13. Soon after a person gets HIV, he or she may have flu-like symptoms.

_____ 14. You can get HIV by donating blood.

_____ 15. You can get HIV from an insect bite.

HIV Facts

How do people get HIV?

HIV is found in blood, semen, vaginal fluids and breast milk. To get HIV, one of these infected fluids has to get inside your body.

There are 3 main ways to get HIV:

- **Sex.** You can get HIV by having sex with a person who has HIV. This includes vaginal, oral or anal sex.

- **Needles.** You can get HIV by sharing drug needles or equipment with a person who has HIV. You can also get HIV by sharing needles for tattoos, piercing, injecting steroids or vitamins or any other reason.

- **Being born with it.** Babies can be born with HIV if the mother has HIV. A baby can also get HIV from breastfeeding. A woman with HIV can take medicines to reduce the chances of passing it to her baby.

How you don't get HIV

You don't get HIV from day-to-day contact with someone who has HIV.

- Touching, hugging, kissing on the lips or hanging out with a person who has HIV doesn't put you at risk.

- Wet kissing is safe as long as neither person has sores or cuts in or on the mouth. HIV is passed in blood, not saliva.

- You can't get HIV from glasses or toilet seats.

- You can't get HIV from giving blood.

- You can't get HIV from mosquitoes or other insects.

How can you tell if someone has HIV?

You can't tell if people have HIV by looking at them. Most people with HIV look healthy, act healthy and feel healthy. Many people who have HIV don't even know they have it.

A simple test can tell if a person has HIV. In many states, teens can get the test without parents' permission. You can get more information about the HIV test from your state or local health department or AIDS agency.

What are the symptoms of HIV?

Many people who have HIV don't have symptoms at first or for a long time. They may not start to feel sick for many years. Sometimes people living with HIV go through periods of being sick and then feel fine again.

Some people go through an illness a few weeks to a few months after they first get HIV.

Symptoms can include:

- Fever
- Chills
- Rash
- Sweating at night
- Muscle aches
- Sore throat
- Fatigue (feeling very tired)
- Swollen lymph nodes
- Sores in the mouth

After the first infection, the virus becomes less active, but is still in the body. **During this period, many people don't have any symptoms of HIV.** This period can last up to 10 years or more. But they can still pass HIV to a sex partner.

(continued)

As HIV infection progresses many people begin to suffer symptoms. Most of the severe long-term consequences, symptoms and illnesses people with HIV experience come from the infections that attack a damaged immune system. People with HIV can take medications to help slow down HIV in the body and treat symptoms.

You can protect yourself

Here are things you can do to help keep from getting HIV:

- **Don't have sex.** This is called abstinence. It means no vaginal, anal or oral sex. It doesn't mean you can't be close, but it does mean keeping somebody else's blood, semen or vaginal fluids out of your body.

- **Practice monogamy.** This means having sex with only one person who doesn't have HIV. Neither of you should ever have sex or share needles with anyone else.

- **Use latex or plastic condoms.** A condom is a sheath that covers a man's penis during sex to keep semen from entering his partner's body. For those who choose to have sex, latex or plastic condoms can help reduce the risk of HIV.

- **Talk with your partner.** Talking may seem hard to do. But if two people decide together to not have sex, to use condoms and/or to have sex only with each other, the plan is more likely to work.

- **Never share needles** for injecting drugs, body piercing, tattooing or any other reason.

- **Always wear rubber gloves when cleaning up spilled blood.**

- **Avoid alcohol and other drugs.** Being drunk or high makes it hard to make careful choices about sex or drug use.

Understanding HIV

Directions: Use what you learned today to answer the questions.

1 What are the 3 ways a person can get HIV?

_____

_____

_____

2 Describe at least 3 symptoms of HIV.

_____

_____

_____

3 Explain what happens to the body over time when a person has HIV.

_____

_____

_____

_____

_____

_____

_____

_____

4 List at least 1 behavior in each of these risk categories, and explain why it carries that level of risk:

No risk: _____

_____

Low risk: _____

_____

Some risk: _____

_____

High risk: _____

_____

(continued)

Understanding HIV

(continued)

5 How can people prevent HIV or reduce their risk?

_____

_____

_____

_____

_____

_____

6 Is it safe to be friends with someone who has HIV? Why or why not?

_____

_____

_____

_____

_____

_____

_____

Self-Check

- ☐ I summarized the 3 ways a person can get HIV.
- ☐ I described at least 3 symptoms of HIV.
- ☐ I explained what happens to the body over time when a person has HIV.
- ☐ I listed at least 1 behavior in each of the risk categories and explained why it carries that risk.
- ☐ I explained how to prevent or reduce the risk of HIV.
- ☐ I explained whether it's safe to be friends with someone who has HIV and why.

22

HEALTH *Smart.* High School

It's Your Call:
Taking or Avoiding Sexual Risks

Directions: Your class is going to collectively write an article that will promote sexual responsibility and point out some of the factors that can either protect teens from taking sexual risks, or make them more likely to participate in sexual risk behaviors. You'll be responsible for writing about the factor your group was first assigned in the brainstorming activity.

Write a draft on your own first. Use what you've learned to write about at least 5 ways your assigned factor can influence sexual choices. In what positive ways could it help protect a person from taking sexual risks? In what negative ways might it make a person more likely to take sexual risks? Then explain how the factor can either support sexual responsibility or lead to sexual risks, and give at least 2 specific examples.

When you've written your draft, you'll meet with your group and combine your drafts to come up with a section for the final article.

▶ Draft

The factor my group will write about: _____

These are some positive ways this factor can influence people's choices about sex:

_____
_____
_____
_____
_____
_____
_____

These are some negative ways this factor can influence people's choices about sex:

_____
_____
_____
_____
_____
_____
_____

(continued)

It's Your Call:
Taking or Avoiding Sexual Risks
(continued)

How this factor can support sexual responsiblitiy:

_____

_____

_____

_____

_____

_____

Examples:

_____

_____

_____

_____

_____

_____

How this factor can make a person more lilely to to take sexual risks:

_____

_____

_____

_____

_____

_____

Examples:

_____

_____

_____

_____

_____

_____

Self-Check
☐ I clearly described at least 5 positive and/or negative ways this factor can influence sexual choices.

☐ I explained how the factor supports sexual responsibility and gave at least 2 examples.

☐ I explained how this factor might make a person more likely to take sexual risks and gave at least 2 examples.

HEALTH *Smart.* High School

Partner Stories: Rate the Risk

Directions: Read each story and rate the risk of STD on a scale from 0 (no risk) to 3 (very high risk). Explain each of your ratings. If a couple is at risk for STD, suggest at least 1 thing they could do to help lower that risk. Then answer the question.

▶ Anita and Duane

Anita and Duane have been girlfriend and boyfriend since ninth grade. They kiss and hug, but don't do any other sexual touching. They've both decided that being abstinent is the best choice for them right now. They feel that waiting is helping their relationship grow stronger.

STD Risk: **0   1   2   3**

Why?

_____

_____

_____

What could they do to reduce the risk?

_____

_____

▶ Calvin and Natalie

Calvin and Natalie are together and have a sexual relationship. Last week, Natalie was away on a school trip. Calvin hooked up with Marta at a party and they had sex. Later in the week, he went out with his old girlfriend Bianca and had sex with her too. Calvin's glad Natalie will be home soon, because he likes her best.

STD Risk: **0   1   2   3**

Why?

_____

_____

_____

What could they do to reduce the risk?

_____

_____

_____

(continued)

Partner Stories: Rate the Risk

(continued)

▶ Morgan and Alex

Morgan and Alex have been together for 2 years. They have sex, but only with each other. Morgan has never had sex with anyone else. Alex had sex in a previous relationship, but that relationship broke up 8 months before Alex got together with Morgan.

STD Risk: **0   1   2   3**

Why?

_____

_____

_____

What could they do to reduce the risk?

_____

_____

_____

▶ Samantha and Mateo

Samantha used to be in a sexual relationship with Luke. As soon as she broke up with him, she got involved with Carlos and they started having sex. Then she met Mateo. Samantha liked Mateo a lot, but wasn't sure she was ready to leave Carlos. After a few weeks of seeing both guys and having sex with both of them, she broke up with Carlos. She's been having sex only with Mateo since then.

STD Risk: **0   1   2   3**

Why?

_____

_____

_____

What could they do to reduce the risk?

_____

_____

_____

HEALTH*Smart.* High School

Partner Stories: Rate the Risk

(continued)

▶ Dory and Leslie

Dory and Leslie were both in monogamous sexual relationships with other people when they met. So, even though they were attracted to each other, they were just friends for a long time. After Dory's relationship broke up, they talked about getting together, but Leslie didn't feel right about it. Then, about 6 months later, Leslie's relationship ended too, and Dory and Leslie started going out right away.

STD Risk: **0**   **1**   **2**   **3**

Why?

_____

_____

_____

What could they do to reduce the risk?

_____

_____

_____

Question:

Why is it important for partners to share the responsibility for protecting themselves by being abstinent or taking steps to reduce their risk of STD?

_____

_____

_____

_____

_____

_____

_____

_____

Self-Check

☐ I rated the risk of STD for all 5 couples, explained my ratings, and suggested at least 1 thing they could do to lower the risk.

☐ I explained why it's important for partners to share responsibility for protecting themselves.

What to Know About Testing

Directions: Read about your assigned test and answer the questions about it. Then share the information you learned with the other members of your group, and take notes on the tests they read about.

▶ **Circle which test you researched:**   **HIV   STD   Pregnancy**

How is the test done? _____

How long does it take to get the results back? _____

How are people told about their results? _____

Are teens' parents told about the test or the results? _____

How does a person know if he/she needs to be tested? _____

_____

Notes: _____

_____

▶ **Test:** _____

How is the test done? _____

How long does it take to get the results back? _____

How are people told about their results? _____

Are teens' parents told about the test or the results? _____

How does a person know if he/she needs to be tested? _____

_____

Notes: _____

_____

▶ **Test:** _____

How is the test done? _____

How long does it take to get the results back? _____

How are people told about their results? _____

Are teens' parents told about the test or the results? _____

How does a person know if he/she needs to be tested? _____

_____

Notes: _____

_____

Check Out a Clinic

> **Directions:** Call or go to a clinic, or visit the clinic website, to gather the information. Then evaluate your experience.

Name of clinic: _____

Clinic address: _____

Phone: _____

Website: _____

If you spoke to someone at the clinic, write his or her name here: _____

What are the clinic's hours? _____

What services are available at this clinic?

☐ STD testing   ☐ Pregnancy testing   ☐ Birth control services

☐ HIV testing   ☐ STD treatment   ☐ Other services: _____

How much does a routine exam or consultation cost? _____

What's the clinic policy about confidentiality? _____

_____

_____

How comfortable did you feel visiting or calling this clinic? (Check one.)

☐ Uncomfortable   ☐ Somewhat comfortable   ☐ Very comfortable

What made it comfortable or uncomfortable? _____

_____

Would you recommend this clinic to a friend who needed information or services?

☐ Yes   ☐ No   Why or why not? _____

Other notes or information about the clinic you want to add to your report:

_____

_____

_____

_____

> **Self-Check**
> ☐ I provided all the information about the clinic and the services it provides.
> ☐ I explained what made visiting or calling the clinic comfortable or uncomfortable.
> ☐ I explained why I would or wouldn't recommend this clinic to a friend.

In Their Own Words
Getting Tested

Directions: "In Their Own Words" is a local radio program that features the voices of teens like you talking to and helping other teens be safe and healthy. The topic for the upcoming program is sexual responsibility and pregnancy and STD/HIV testing. You're going to be one of the teens who'll be interviewed about these topics.

Use this activity sheet to organize your thoughts and prepare the talking points you want to be sure to cover during your speaking time. The questions are ones the host of the program will be asking you during the show.

1 Can you describe at least 2 ways in which knowing your STD/HIV status or that of a potential sexual partner is part of being a sexually responsible teen?

_____

_____

_____

2 What are the basic steps involved in getting tested for HIV, other STD and pregnancy?

_____

_____

_____

3 What kind of help or counseling is available for people who want to get tested and why is it important?

_____

_____

_____

_____

4 What are at least 3 reasons sexually active people should be tested for HIV and other STD?

_____

_____

_____

5 Where are at least 2 places teens in our community can go to be tested for HIV, other STD and pregnancy?

_____

_____

_____

Self-Check

☐ I described at least 2 ways knowing my STD/HIV status or that of a partner is part of being sexually responsible.

☐ I described the basic steps involved in getting tested for HIV, other STD and pregnancy.

☐ I described the counseling available and explained why it's important.

☐ I identified at least 2 local clinics or agencies where teens can be tested.

Condom Checklist

Directions: Place an X in the box that best indicates how well your partner demonstrates the correct way to put on a condom.

Your Name _____

Your Partner's Name _____

Steps	The step was completely demonstrated	The step was partially demonstrated	The step was not demonstrated at all
Check the expiration date on the condom package.	☐	☐	☐
Open the package and take out the condom carefully.	☐	☐	☐
Check to see which way the condom unrolls.	☐	☐	☐
Pinch the tip of the condom to keep air out.	☐	☐	☐
Leave ½ inch of room at the tip of the condom.	☐	☐	☐
Unroll the condom onto the index and middle finger of your hand. Unroll the condom all the way down to the bottom of your fingers.	☐	☐	☐

Notes:

_____

_____

_____

_____

_____

Self-Check

☐ I evaluated all 6 steps for proper condom use demonstrated by my partner.

Condom Challenges & Solutions

Directions: In your group, identify 2 things that may make it difficult for young people to use condoms. List these in the challenge boxes. Then think of 1 or more solutions for dealing with each challenge. List these in the solution boxes.

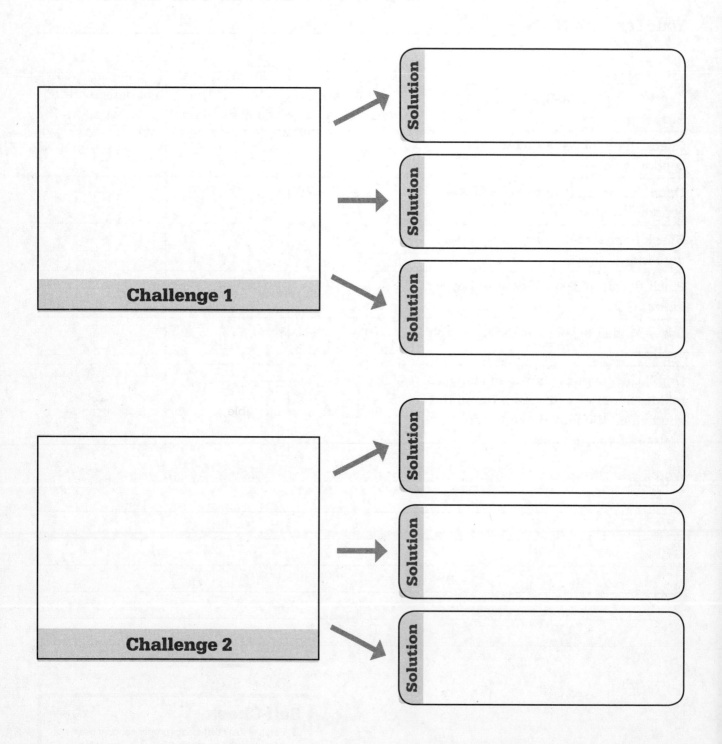

Condom Hunt

> **Directions:** Your assignment is to research the availability of condoms from a local store or other resource. Complete the form and answer the questions for your report.

Name of store/agency: _____

Location: _____

Business hours: _____

Describe where the condoms are located: _____

_____

_____

What kinds of condoms are sold here? (List up to 4 brands or types.)

Brand Name	Price	Lubricated?	Contains Spermicide?	Expiration Date
_____	_____	☐ Yes ☐ No	☐ Yes ☐ No	_____
_____	_____	☐ Yes ☐ No	☐ Yes ☐ No	_____
_____	_____	☐ Yes ☐ No	☐ Yes ☐ No	_____
_____	_____	☐ Yes ☐ No	☐ Yes ☐ No	_____

How comfortable would you feel getting condoms here? (circle one)

Very comfortable	Fairly comfortable	Somewhat uncomfortable	Very uncomfortable
1	**2**	**3**	**4**

Would you recommend that a friend get condoms here? ☐ Yes ☐ No

Explain why or why not: _____

_____

_____

_____

_____

_____

> ## Self-Check
> ☐ I provided all the information about obtaining condoms.
> ☐ I explained why I would or wouldn't recommend this clinic to a friend.

Negotiating Condom Use

> **Directions:** At some time in your life, you may need to talk to a partner about condoms. It helps to be prepared. For each step below, write a specific strategy for negotiating condom use.

(1) Know what you want and describe it. In your own words, what are your views about using condoms?

_____

_____

_____

_____

(2) Communicate what's acceptable and what's not. What would you expect from yourself and from your partner in terms of condom use?

_____

_____

_____

(3) Present rational, consistent ideas that support your position. Explain why condoms are effective and summarize why using them consistently and correctly is important for:

- Reducing the risk of pregnancy
- Reducing the risk of HIV
- Reducing the risk of other STD

> ### Fact
> Studies show that young people who believe their peers are using condoms are much more likely to use condoms themselves.

_____

_____

_____

_____

_____

_____

_____

_____

_____

_____

Negotiating Condom Use

(continued)

④ Try to understand the other person's point of view. See where you have common ground. What are possible objections a partner might have, and how might you respond to those objections?

_____

_____

_____

_____

> **Fact**
> After abstinence, condoms are the next best way to reduce the risk of HIV and other STD.

_____

_____

_____

_____

⑤ Look for ways to compromise that are acceptable to you. What are areas where you would compromise? What are areas where you wouldn't compromise?

_____

_____

_____

_____

_____

_____

⑥ Come to an agreement OR Give a clear NO message. If you couldn't reach an agreement about using condoms, what would you say and do?

_____

_____

_____

_____

_____

_____

Self-Check
- ☐ I clearly described my views about using condoms and explained what is and isn't acceptable.
- ☐ I explained why condoms are effective and why using them is important.

Not Without a Condom

Directions: Read the Situation. Then fill in the "You" lines using negotiation skills for saying NO. Finish the script by using skills for negotiating to write lines for you and your partner that show a successful negotiation either to use condoms or not have sex. Be sure to use at least 4 of the skills you've learned.

▶ Situation

You and your partner are at your partner's house late at night after a party. No one else is home. You begin kissing and touching. Your partner is pressuring you to have sex. You've made a promise to yourself never to have sex without using a condom and have told your partner this.

You: Do you have condoms?

Your Partner: No, but don't worry. Nothing will happen.

You: I won't have sex without a condom.

Your Partner: Condoms will spoil the mood. Come on. It'll be OK.

You: _____

                   _____

                   _____

Your Partner: We don't have any diseases.

You: _____

                   _____

                   _____

                   _____

Your Partner: _____

                   _____

You: _____

                   _____

                   _____

                   _____

HEALTHSmart. High School

Not Without a Condom

(continued)

Your Partner: _____

You: _____

_____

_____

_____

Your Partner: _____

You: _____

_____

_____

_____

Your Partner: _____

You: _____

_____

_____

_____

Self-Check

☐ I wrote a clear and specific response that uses skills for saying NO to the first 2 pressure lines.

☐ I wrote lines that show a successful negotiation to use condoms or not have sex, using at least 4 negotiation skills.

☐ I presented the lines for both people in a clear and effective way.

My Commitment

> **Directions:** Think about your own life and the choices you can make to help protect yourself from unplanned pregnancy, HIV and other STD. Check off and answer the questions, then fill out and sign the commitment form.

☐ I understand that sexual abstinence is the safest, most effective way to avoid pregnancy, HIV and other STD because:

_____

_____

☐ I know that if I decide to be sexually active, these are at least 4 ways I can reduce the risk of pregnancy, HIV and other STD:

_____

_____

_____

_____

My Commitment

I, _____, will make the following commitment to help protect myself from unplanned pregnancy, HIV and other STD:

_____

_____

These are 3 steps I will take to keep my commitment:

1. _____

   How this step will help me: _____

   _____

2. _____

   How this step will help me: _____

   _____

3. _____

   How this step will help me: _____

   _____

Signature: _____

Date: _____

Self-Check

☐ I explained why sexual abstinence is the safest most effective way to avoid pregnancy, HIV and other STD.

☐ I described at least 4 ways to reduce the risk of pregnancy, HIV and other STD.

☐ I wrote a clear commitment, listed 3 steps I'll take to keep it, and explained how each step will help me.

Advocating for My Friends
Part 1

> **Directions:** Explain why you think it's important for teens to protect themselves from pregnancy, HIV and other STD, and support your view with accurate information based on what you've been learning. Then think about what behaviors will help protect your friends and other teens, and the message you'd like to send to help them graduate from high school without getting pregnant, getting someone pregnant or becoming infected with HIV or another STD.

1 Why is it important for teens to protect themselves from pregnancy, HIV and other STD?

_____
_____
_____
_____

2 What are 3 facts that support your view?

_____
_____
_____
_____

3 What are at least 2 behaviors that will help teens protect themselves or reduce their risk?

_____
_____
_____
_____

4 What's one important and clear message you'd like to send to your friends and other teens about protecting themselves from pregnancy, HIV and other STD?

_____
_____
_____
_____

Advocating for My Friends
Part 2

> **Directions:** Work with your group to come up with one clear and convincing message you want to share with your friends and other teens. Be sure to shape the message and present it in a form that will appeal to your target audience. Then plan what each person in your group will do and how you'll work together to help create or share the message.

What is your message to teens?

_____

_____

_____

Why will this message appeal to your target audience?

_____

_____

_____

How will you share your message to influence and support others?
(For example, poster, letter, poem, song, rap, video, etc.)

_____

_____

_____

How will your group work together to deliver your message?

_____

_____

_____

_____

_____

_____

_____

Self-Check

☐ I explained why it's important for teens to protect themselves against pregnancy, HIV and other STD.

☐ I listed behaviors that will help teens protect themselves.

☐ I stated an important and clear message about protecting yourself from pregnancy, HIV and other STD.

☐ We wrote a message that will appeal to our target audience and explained why it will appeal to them.

☐ We chose a way to share our message that will appeal to our audience.

☐ We planned what each person will do and created our message.